THIS JOURNAL BELONGS TO:

_____

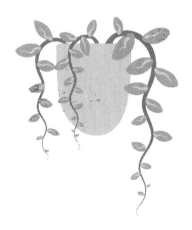

Find us on social media @luckysproutpress
or visit luckysproutpress.com

HOUSE PLANT
journal

HOUSE PLANT INVENTORY

PLANT NAME: **LOCATION:**

HOUSE PLANT INVENTORY

PLANT NAME: **LOCATION:**

HOUSE PLANT INVENTORY

PLANT NAME: **LOCATION:**

HOUSE PLANT INVENTORY

PLANT NAME:

LOCATION:

HOUSE PLANT INVENTORY

PLANT NAME: **LOCATION:**

HOUSE PLANT INVENTORY

PLANT NAME: **LOCATION:**

WATERING DATES

FERTILIZING DATES

NICKNAME:

PLANT NAME:

WATER NEEDED:

LIGHT NEEDED:

MISTING: ☐ DAILY ☐ WEEKLY ☐ NONE

TIMES REPOTTED: ☐ ☐ ☐ ☐ ☐ ☐

FERTILIZER FREQUENCY:

GROWTH CHART

DATE　　　HEIGHT

SKETCH/LEAF:

DATE ACQUIRED:

WATERING DATES

FERTILIZING DATES

NICKNAME:

PLANT NAME:

WATER NEEDED:

LIGHT NEEDED:

MISTING: ☐ DAILY ☐ WEEKLY ☐ NONE

TIMES REPOTTED: ☐ ☐ ☐ ☐ ☐ ☐

FERTILIZER FREQUENCY:

GROWTH CHART

DATE　　HEIGHT

SKETCH/LEAF:

DATE ACQUIRED:

WATERING DATES

FERTILIZING DATES

NICKNAME:

PLANT NAME:

WATER NEEDED:

LIGHT NEEDED:

MISTING: ☐ DAILY ☐ WEEKLY ☐ NONE

TIMES REPOTTED: ☐ ☐ ☐ ☐ ☐ ☐

FERTILIZER FREQUENCY:

GROWTH CHART

DATE   HEIGHT

SKETCH/LEAF:

DATE ACQUIRED:

WATERING DATES

FERTILIZING DATES

NICKNAME:

PLANT NAME:

WATER NEEDED:

LIGHT NEEDED:

MISTING: ☐ DAILY ☐ WEEKLY ☐ NONE

TIMES REPOTTED: ☐ ☐ ☐ ☐ ☐ ☐

FERTILIZER FREQUENCY:

GROWTH CHART

DATE   HEIGHT

SKETCH/LEAF:

DATE ACQUIRED:

WATERING DATES

FERTILIZING DATES

NICKNAME:

PLANT NAME:

WATER NEEDED:

LIGHT NEEDED:

MISTING: ☐ DAILY ☐ WEEKLY ☐ NONE

TIMES REPOTTED: ☐ ☐ ☐ ☐ ☐ ☐

FERTILIZER FREQUENCY:

GROWTH CHART

DATE   HEIGHT

SKETCH/LEAF:

DATE ACQUIRED:

WATERING DATES

FERTILIZING DATES

NICKNAME:

PLANT NAME:

WATER NEEDED:

LIGHT NEEDED:

MISTING: ☐ DAILY ☐ WEEKLY ☐ NONE

TIMES REPOTTED: ☐ ☐ ☐ ☐ ☐ ☐

FERTILIZER FREQUENCY:

GROWTH CHART

DATE   HEIGHT

SKETCH/LEAF:

DATE ACQUIRED:

WATERING DATES

FERTILIZING DATES

NICKNAME:

PLANT NAME:

WATER NEEDED:

LIGHT NEEDED:

MISTING: ☐ DAILY ☐ WEEKLY ☐ NONE

TIMES REPOTTED: ☐ ☐ ☐ ☐ ☐ ☐

FERTILIZER FREQUENCY:

GROWTH CHART

DATE   HEIGHT

SKETCH/LEAF:

DATE ACQUIRED:

WATERING DATES

FERTILIZING DATES

NICKNAME:

PLANT NAME:

WATER NEEDED:

LIGHT NEEDED:

MISTING: ☐ DAILY ☐ WEEKLY ☐ NONE

TIMES REPOTTED: ☐ ☐ ☐ ☐ ☐ ☐

FERTILIZER FREQUENCY:

GROWTH CHART

DATE　　　HEIGHT

SKETCH/LEAF:

DATE ACQUIRED:

WATERING DATES

FERTILIZING DATES

NICKNAME:

PLANT NAME:

WATER NEEDED:

LIGHT NEEDED:

MISTING: ☐ DAILY ☐ WEEKLY ☐ NONE

TIMES REPOTTED: ☐ ☐ ☐ ☐ ☐ ☐

FERTILIZER FREQUENCY:

GROWTH CHART

DATE   HEIGHT

SKETCH/LEAF:

DATE ACQUIRED:

WATERING DATES

FERTILIZING DATES

NICKNAME:

PLANT NAME:

WATER NEEDED:

LIGHT NEEDED:

MISTING: ☐ DAILY ☐ WEEKLY ☐ NONE

TIMES REPOTTED: ☐ ☐ ☐ ☐ ☐ ☐

FERTILIZER FREQUENCY:

GROWTH CHART

DATE   HEIGHT

SKETCH/LEAF:

DATE ACQUIRED:

WATERING DATES

FERTILIZING DATES

NICKNAME:

PLANT NAME:

WATER NEEDED:

LIGHT NEEDED:

MISTING: ☐ DAILY ☐ WEEKLY ☐ NONE

TIMES REPOTTED: ☐ ☐ ☐ ☐ ☐ ☐

FERTILIZER FREQUENCY:

GROWTH CHART

DATE   HEIGHT

SKETCH/LEAF:

DATE ACQUIRED:

WATERING DATES

FERTILIZING DATES

NICKNAME:

PLANT NAME:

WATER NEEDED:

LIGHT NEEDED:

MISTING: ☐ DAILY ☐ WEEKLY ☐ NONE

TIMES REPOTTED: ☐ ☐ ☐ ☐ ☐ ☐

FERTILIZER FREQUENCY:

GROWTH CHART

DATE   HEIGHT

SKETCH/LEAF:

DATE ACQUIRED:

WATERING DATES

FERTILIZING DATES

NICKNAME:

PLANT NAME:

WATER NEEDED:

LIGHT NEEDED:

MISTING: ☐ DAILY ☐ WEEKLY ☐ NONE

TIMES REPOTTED: ☐ ☐ ☐ ☐ ☐ ☐

FERTILIZER FREQUENCY:

GROWTH CHART

DATE   HEIGHT

SKETCH/LEAF:

DATE ACQUIRED:

WATERING DATES

FERTILIZING DATES

NICKNAME:

PLANT NAME:

WATER NEEDED:

LIGHT NEEDED:

MISTING: ☐ DAILY ☐ WEEKLY ☐ NONE

TIMES REPOTTED: ☐ ☐ ☐ ☐ ☐ ☐

FERTILIZER FREQUENCY:

GROWTH CHART

DATE   HEIGHT

SKETCH/LEAF:

DATE ACQUIRED:

WATERING DATES

FERTILIZING DATES

NICKNAME:

PLANT NAME:

WATER NEEDED:

LIGHT NEEDED:

MISTING: ☐ DAILY ☐ WEEKLY ☐ NONE

TIMES REPOTTED: ☐ ☐ ☐ ☐ ☐ ☐

FERTILIZER FREQUENCY:

GROWTH CHART

DATE   HEIGHT

SKETCH/LEAF:

DATE ACQUIRED:

WATERING DATES

FERTILIZING DATES

NICKNAME:

PLANT NAME:

WATER NEEDED:

LIGHT NEEDED:

MISTING: ☐ DAILY ☐ WEEKLY ☐ NONE

TIMES REPOTTED: ☐ ☐ ☐ ☐ ☐ ☐

FERTILIZER FREQUENCY:

GROWTH CHART

DATE · HEIGHT

SKETCH/LEAF:

DATE ACQUIRED:

WATERING DATES

FERTILIZING DATES

NICKNAME:

PLANT NAME:

WATER NEEDED:

LIGHT NEEDED:

MISTING: ☐ DAILY ☐ WEEKLY ☐ NONE

TIMES REPOTTED: ☐ ☐ ☐ ☐ ☐ ☐

FERTILIZER FREQUENCY:

GROWTH CHART

DATE   HEIGHT

SKETCH/LEAF:

DATE ACQUIRED:

WATERING DATES

FERTILIZING DATES

NICKNAME:

PLANT NAME:

WATER NEEDED:

LIGHT NEEDED:

MISTING:
[ ] DAILY [ ] WEEKLY [ ] NONE

TIMES REPOTTED: [ ] [ ] [ ] [ ] [ ] [ ]

FERTILIZER FREQUENCY:

GROWTH CHART

DATE   HEIGHT

SKETCH/LEAF:

DATE ACQUIRED:

WATERING DATES

FERTILIZING DATES

NICKNAME:

PLANT NAME:

WATER NEEDED:

LIGHT NEEDED:

MISTING: ☐ DAILY ☐ WEEKLY ☐ NONE

TIMES REPOTTED: ☐ ☐ ☐ ☐ ☐ ☐

FERTILIZER FREQUENCY:

GROWTH CHART

DATE   HEIGHT

SKETCH/LEAF:

DATE ACQUIRED:

WATERING DATES

FERTILIZING DATES

NICKNAME:

PLANT NAME:

WATER NEEDED:

LIGHT NEEDED:

MISTING: ☐ DAILY ☐ WEEKLY ☐ NONE

TIMES REPOTTED: ☐ ☐ ☐ ☐ ☐ ☐

FERTILIZER FREQUENCY:

GROWTH CHART

DATE　　　HEIGHT

SKETCH/LEAF:

DATE ACQUIRED:

WATERING DATES

FERTILIZING DATES

NICKNAME:

PLANT NAME:

WATER NEEDED:

LIGHT NEEDED:

MISTING:
☐ DAILY ☐ WEEKLY ☐ NONE

TIMES REPOTTED:
☐ ☐ ☐ ☐ ☐ ☐

FERTILIZER FREQUENCY:

GROWTH CHART
DATE   HEIGHT

SKETCH/LEAF:

DATE ACQUIRED:

WATERING DATES

FERTILIZING DATES

NICKNAME:

PLANT NAME:

WATER NEEDED:

LIGHT NEEDED:

MISTING: □ DAILY   □ WEEKLY   □ NONE

TIMES REPOTTED: □ □ □ □ □ □

FERTILIZER FREQUENCY:

GROWTH CHART

DATE   HEIGHT

SKETCH/LEAF:

DATE ACQUIRED:

WATERING DATES

FERTILIZING DATES

NICKNAME:

PLANT NAME:

WATER NEEDED:

LIGHT NEEDED:

MISTING: ☐ DAILY ☐ WEEKLY ☐ NONE

TIMES REPOTTED: ☐ ☐ ☐ ☐ ☐ ☐

FERTILIZER FREQUENCY:

GROWTH CHART

DATE   HEIGHT

SKETCH/LEAF:

DATE ACQUIRED:

WATERING DATES

FERTILIZING DATES

NICKNAME:

PLANT NAME:

WATER NEEDED:

LIGHT NEEDED:

MISTING: ☐ DAILY ☐ WEEKLY ☐ NONE

TIMES REPOTTED: ☐ ☐ ☐ ☐ ☐ ☐

FERTILIZER FREQUENCY:

GROWTH CHART

DATE   HEIGHT

SKETCH/LEAF:

DATE ACQUIRED:

WATERING DATES

FERTILIZING DATES

NICKNAME:

PLANT NAME:

WATER NEEDED:

LIGHT NEEDED:

MISTING: ☐ DAILY ☐ WEEKLY ☐ NONE

TIMES REPOTTED: ☐ ☐ ☐ ☐ ☐ ☐

FERTILIZER FREQUENCY:

GROWTH CHART

DATE   HEIGHT

SKETCH/LEAF:

DATE ACQUIRED:

WATERING DATES

FERTILIZING DATES

NICKNAME:

PLANT NAME:

WATER NEEDED:

LIGHT NEEDED:

MISTING: ☐ DAILY ☐ WEEKLY ☐ NONE

TIMES REPOTTED: ☐ ☐ ☐ ☐ ☐ ☐

FERTILIZER FREQUENCY:

GROWTH CHART

DATE   HEIGHT

SKETCH/LEAF:

DATE ACQUIRED:

WATERING DATES

FERTILIZING DATES

NICKNAME:

PLANT NAME:

WATER NEEDED:

LIGHT NEEDED:

MISTING: ☐ DAILY ☐ WEEKLY ☐ NONE

TIMES REPOTTED: ☐ ☐ ☐ ☐ ☐ ☐

FERTILIZER FREQUENCY:

GROWTH CHART

DATE   HEIGHT

SKETCH/LEAF:

DATE ACQUIRED:

WATERING DATES

FERTILIZING DATES

NICKNAME:

PLANT NAME:

WATER NEEDED:

LIGHT NEEDED:

MISTING: ☐ DAILY ☐ WEEKLY ☐ NONE

TIMES REPOTTED: ☐ ☐ ☐ ☐ ☐ ☐

FERTILIZER FREQUENCY:

GROWTH CHART

DATE   HEIGHT

SKETCH/LEAF:

DATE ACQUIRED:

WATERING DATES

FERTILIZING DATES

NICKNAME:

PLANT NAME:

WATER NEEDED:

LIGHT NEEDED:

MISTING: ☐ DAILY ☐ WEEKLY ☐ NONE

TIMES REPOTTED: ☐ ☐ ☐ ☐ ☐ ☐

FERTILIZER FREQUENCY:

GROWTH CHART

DATE   HEIGHT

SKETCH/LEAF:

DATE ACQUIRED:

WATERING DATES

FERTILIZING DATES

NICKNAME:

PLANT NAME:

WATER NEEDED:

LIGHT NEEDED:

MISTING: ☐ DAILY ☐ WEEKLY ☐ NONE

TIMES REPOTTED: ☐ ☐ ☐ ☐ ☐ ☐

FERTILIZER FREQUENCY:

GROWTH CHART

DATE · HEIGHT

SKETCH/LEAF:

DATE ACQUIRED:

WATERING DATES

FERTILIZING DATES

NICKNAME:

PLANT NAME:

WATER NEEDED:

LIGHT NEEDED:

MISTING: ☐ DAILY ☐ WEEKLY ☐ NONE

TIMES REPOTTED: ☐ ☐ ☐ ☐ ☐ ☐

FERTILIZER FREQUENCY:

GROWTH CHART

DATE   HEIGHT

SKETCH/LEAF:

DATE ACQUIRED:

WATERING DATES

FERTILIZING DATES

NICKNAME:

PLANT NAME:

WATER NEEDED:

LIGHT NEEDED:

MISTING: ☐ DAILY ☐ WEEKLY ☐ NONE

TIMES REPOTTED: ☐ ☐ ☐ ☐ ☐ ☐

FERTILIZER FREQUENCY:

GROWTH CHART

DATE   HEIGHT

SKETCH/LEAF:

DATE ACQUIRED:

WATERING DATES

FERTILIZING DATES

NICKNAME:

PLANT NAME:

WATER NEEDED:

LIGHT NEEDED:

MISTING: ☐ DAILY ☐ WEEKLY ☐ NONE

TIMES REPOTTED: ☐ ☐ ☐ ☐ ☐ ☐

FERTILIZER FREQUENCY:

GROWTH CHART

DATE   HEIGHT

SKETCH/LEAF:

DATE ACQUIRED:

WATERING DATES

FERTILIZING DATES

NICKNAME:

PLANT NAME:

WATER NEEDED:

LIGHT NEEDED:

MISTING: ☐ DAILY ☐ WEEKLY ☐ NONE

TIMES REPOTTED: ☐ ☐ ☐ ☐ ☐ ☐

FERTILIZER FREQUENCY:

GROWTH CHART

DATE · HEIGHT

SKETCH/LEAF:

DATE ACQUIRED:

WATERING DATES

FERTILIZING DATES

NICKNAME:

PLANT NAME:

WATER NEEDED:

LIGHT NEEDED:

MISTING: ☐ DAILY ☐ WEEKLY ☐ NONE

TIMES REPOTTED: ☐ ☐ ☐ ☐ ☐ ☐

FERTILIZER FREQUENCY:

GROWTH CHART

DATE | HEIGHT

SKETCH/LEAF:

DATE ACQUIRED:

WATERING DATES

FERTILIZING DATES

NICKNAME:

PLANT NAME:

WATER NEEDED:

LIGHT NEEDED:

MISTING: ☐ DAILY ☐ WEEKLY ☐ NONE

TIMES REPOTTED: ☐ ☐ ☐ ☐ ☐ ☐

FERTILIZER FREQUENCY:

GROWTH CHART

DATE   •   HEIGHT

SKETCH/LEAF:

DATE ACQUIRED:

WATERING DATES

FERTILIZING DATES

NICKNAME:

PLANT NAME:

WATER NEEDED:

LIGHT NEEDED:

MISTING: ☐ DAILY ☐ WEEKLY ☐ NONE

TIMES REPOTTED: ☐ ☐ ☐ ☐ ☐ ☐

FERTILIZER FREQUENCY:

GROWTH CHART

DATE   HEIGHT

SKETCH/LEAF:

DATE ACQUIRED:

WATERING DATES

FERTILIZING DATES

NICKNAME:

PLANT NAME:

WATER NEEDED:

LIGHT NEEDED:

MISTING: ☐ DAILY ☐ WEEKLY ☐ NONE

TIMES REPOTTED: ☐ ☐ ☐ ☐ ☐ ☐

FERTILIZER FREQUENCY:

GROWTH CHART

DATE   HEIGHT

SKETCH/LEAF:

DATE ACQUIRED:

WATERING DATES

FERTILIZING DATES

NICKNAME:

PLANT NAME:

WATER NEEDED:

LIGHT NEEDED:

MISTING: ☐ DAILY ☐ WEEKLY ☐ NONE

TIMES REPOTTED: ☐ ☐ ☐ ☐ ☐ ☐

FERTILIZER FREQUENCY:

GROWTH CHART

DATE   HEIGHT

SKETCH/LEAF:

DATE ACQUIRED:

WATERING DATES

FERTILIZING DATES

NICKNAME:

PLANT NAME:

WATER NEEDED:

LIGHT NEEDED:

MISTING: ☐ DAILY ☐ WEEKLY ☐ NONE

TIMES REPOTTED: ☐ ☐ ☐ ☐ ☐ ☐

FERTILIZER FREQUENCY:

GROWTH CHART

DATE · HEIGHT

SKETCH/LEAF:

DATE ACQUIRED:

WATERING DATES

FERTILIZING DATES

NICKNAME:

PLANT NAME:

WATER NEEDED:

LIGHT NEEDED:

MISTING: ☐ DAILY ☐ WEEKLY ☐ NONE

TIMES REPOTTED: ☐ ☐ ☐ ☐ ☐ ☐

FERTILIZER FREQUENCY:

GROWTH CHART

DATE   HEIGHT

SKETCH/LEAF:

DATE ACQUIRED:

WATERING DATES

FERTILIZING DATES

NICKNAME:

PLANT NAME:

WATER NEEDED:

LIGHT NEEDED:

MISTING: ☐ DAILY ☐ WEEKLY ☐ NONE

TIMES REPOTTED: ☐ ☐ ☐ ☐ ☐ ☐

FERTILIZER FREQUENCY:

GROWTH CHART

DATE   HEIGHT

SKETCH/LEAF:

DATE ACQUIRED: